Clairmont @rusytime S.S.

D1450685

©Copyright, 1975, By Bill and Gloria Gaither
Published By IMPACT BOOKS
Library of Congress Number 75-18615
ISBN 0-914850-98-9
M0498

All rights reserved, including the right to reproduce this book or
portions thereof in any form without written permission of the
Publisher.

you're Something Special!

by Bill & Gloria Gaither

Illustrated by ALETHA JONES

impact books

When Jesus sent you to us,
We loved you from the start,

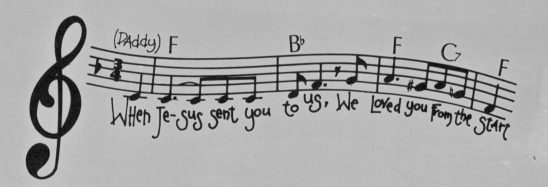

You were just a bit of sunshine from heaven to our hearts

you Were just A Bit of Sun-Shine From Heav-en to our Hearts

Not just another baby—
'Cause since the world
began there's been something
very special
for you in His plan.

That's why
He made you special
You're the only one of your kind;
God gave you a body
And a bright healthy mind.

He had a special purpose
that he wanted you to find,
so he made you something special
You're the only one of your kind.

I have a little sister
who's not at all like me,
She can write a
lovely poem
but I can climb a tree;

My brother, tho,' he's diff'rent,
with Freckles on his nose;

When my questions needed answers,
He's the one who knows.

That's why
I'm something special
I'm the only one of my kind;
God gave me a body and
a bright healthy mind.

He had a special purpose
that He wanted me to find,
so He made me something special
I'm the only one of my kind,

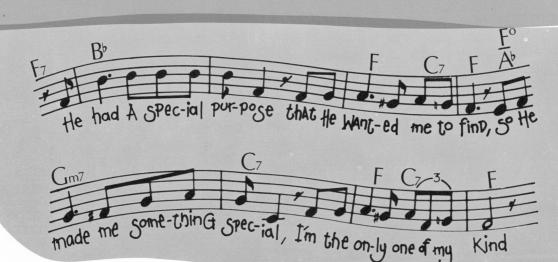

My Daddy mows the back yard,

My Mommy makes the bed,

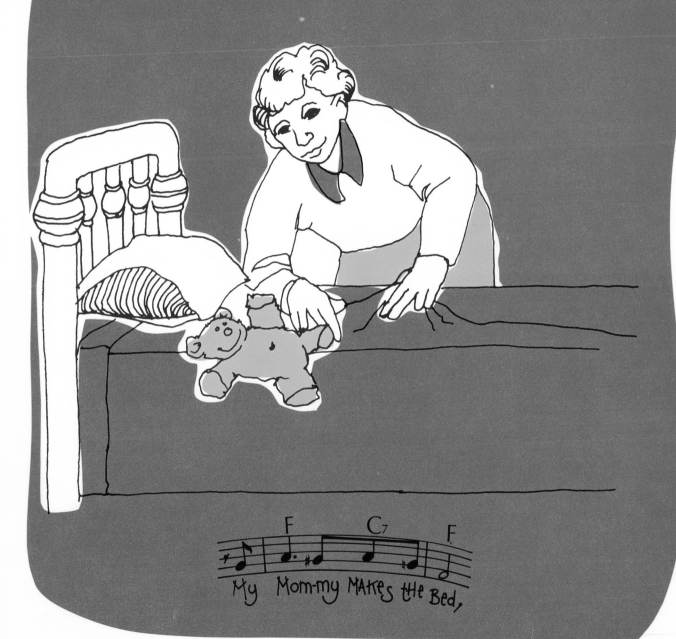

My Brother cleans the play room,

I see our dog gets fed;

And each one needs the other to help him thro' the day

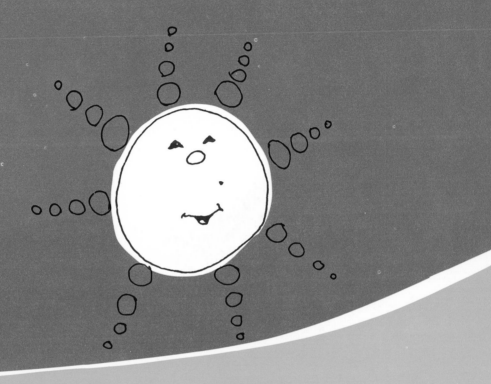

And love must be the reason God planned it just that way.

That's why
I'm something special,
I'm the only one of my kind;
God gave you a body
and a bright healthy mind.

He had a special purpose
that he wanted me to find,
So He made me something special,
I'm the only one of my kind.

He made you something special,
He made me something special,
He made you something special,
You're the only one of your kind.

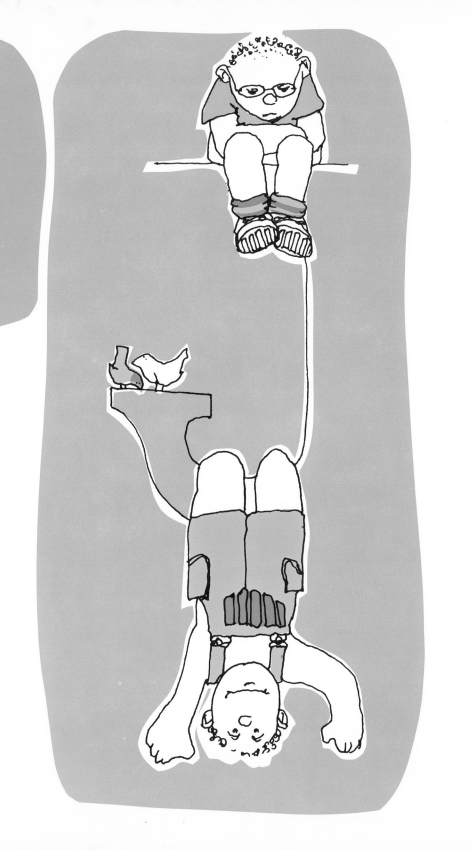